FUN FINDING OUT

THINGS THAT GO

Rosie McCormick   Anthony Lewis

Kingfisher

To Jenna – RMC

In loving memory
of Oscar – AL

KINGFISHER BOOKS
An imprint of Larousse plc
Elsley House, 24-30 Great Titchfield Street, London W1P 7AD

First published by Kingfisher 1997
10 9 8 7 6 5 4 3 2 1

Copyright © Kingfisher Books 1997

A CIP catalogue record for this book is available from the
British Library.

ISBN 0 7534 0141 X

The rights of Rosie McCormick to be identified as author of this
book and Anthony Lewis to be identified as illustrator of this book
have been asserted by them in accordance with the Copyright,
Designs and Patents Act, 1988.

Series editor: Sue Nicholson
Series designer: Kathryn Caulfield

Printed in Singapore

Answers

How many wheels?
Bicycle – 2; Car – 4; Lorry – 6 ;
Tanker – 18

Staying safe
Helmet – head; Reflector band –
body; Protective pads – knees
and elbows

Choosing the right car
1 Mini; 2 Sports car; 3 People
carrier; 4 Jeep

Which boat?
Speedboat

Which line?
1 Green line; 2 Five; 3 Yellow
and striped lines

Contents

On the move

BEEP BEEP! HONK, HONK! RING, RING!
Every day, you can hear the sounds of
all kinds of things that go. Cars, trucks,
trains and planes busily carry people
and goods from place to place. How
many kinds of transport machines
do you know?

Helicopter

Huge container ships carry
goods across the sea.

Trucks and lorries
move heavy loads.

Bus

Lorry

Car

Taxi

Moped

Plane

Planes go faster than trains or ships. They fly to faraway places all over the world.

We choose a different kind of transport depending on how far we want to travel and how fast we want to go.

Train

In busy towns and cities, lots of people travel by train or bus.

How many wheels?

Big, heavy machines need more wheels to support them. How many wheels do these machines have?

Bicycle

Car

Lorry

Tanker

Motorbike

Bicycle

Bicycles are usually used for short journeys, such as going to the park or to school.

Van

On two wheels

A bicycle will go just as fast as its rider can turn the pedals. The pedals turn the chain, the chain turns the back wheel, and the back wheel pushes the bike forwards.

A unicycle has just one wheel.

Mountain bikes have thick tyres which are good for riding across muddy, bumpy ground.

A tricycle has three wheels. Most children ride a trike before they learn how to balance on two wheels.

Staying safe

When riding a bike, you should wear special things to protect your body in case you have an accident.

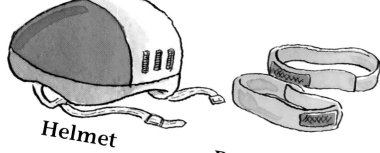

Helmet

Reflector band

Protective pads

Where would you wear these?

Racing bikes have light-weight frames. They are faster than ordinary bikes.

Motorbikes have petrol-powered engines. Some are as big as car engines.

Mopeds have smaller engines than motorbikes. They cannot go as fast.

Skateboard

Roller-skates

Parts of a bike

The handlebars turn the front wheel and steer the bike. The brakes are operated by levers. They slow the bike down.

Saddle

Back light

Reflector

Tyre

Wheel

Handlebars

Front light

Frame

Brake levers

Chain

Pedal

All kinds of cars

Some people need large family cars to fit everyone in. Others prefer smaller cars because they use less fuel and are easier to park in busy cities. Jeeps drive well on bumpy roads. Sports cars go really fast.

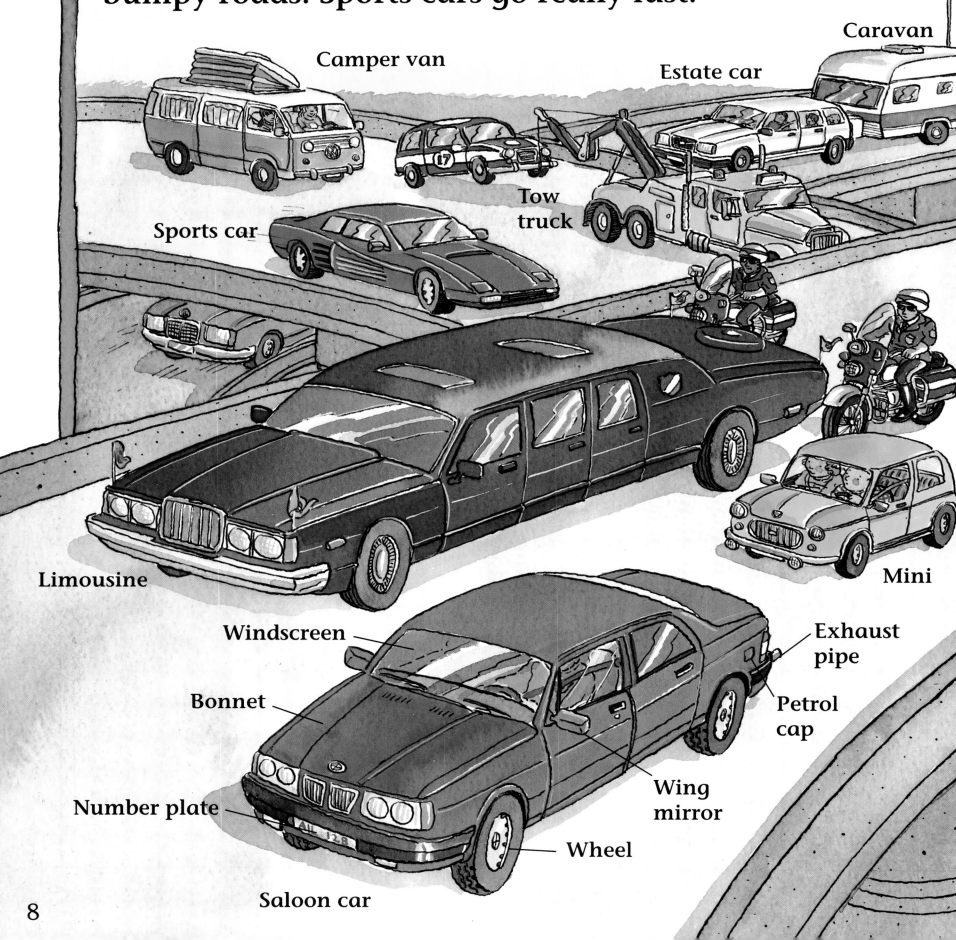

Caravan

Camper van

Estate car

Tow truck

Sports car

Limousine

Mini

Windscreen

Exhaust pipe

Bonnet

Petrol cap

Number plate

Wing mirror

Wheel

Saloon car

A car cannot go without fuel. Most cars use petrol to make them go. Some use diesel fuel.

Van

Taxi

Racing cars

Racing cars are the fastest cars of all. Their streamlined shapes and powerful engines give them extra speed.

People carrier

Jeep

Convertible

Trailer

Hatchback

Choosing the right car

Which car would you choose if you wanted to:

1 Park in a small space?

2 Go very fast?

3 Carry lots of people?

4 Travel across muddy, bumpy ground?

Jeep

Mini

Sports car

People carrier

Fire engines

NEE-NA! NEE-NA! NEE-NA!

Fire engines race, with sirens ringing and lights flashing, to put out fires and to rescue people and pets. Police and ambulance crews often rush to a fire as well. They are there to keep people out of danger and to help in case anyone is hurt.

Breathing in smoke is dangerous, so firefighters wear special masks and carry tanks of oxygen.

Oxygen tank

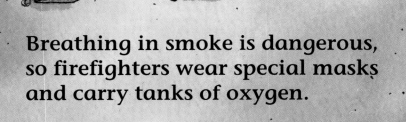

Firefighting plane

A firefighting plane is used to put out forest fires.

1 The plane lands on a lake and fills its tanks with water.

2 It drops the water on to the fire, then returns to the lake to refill.

10

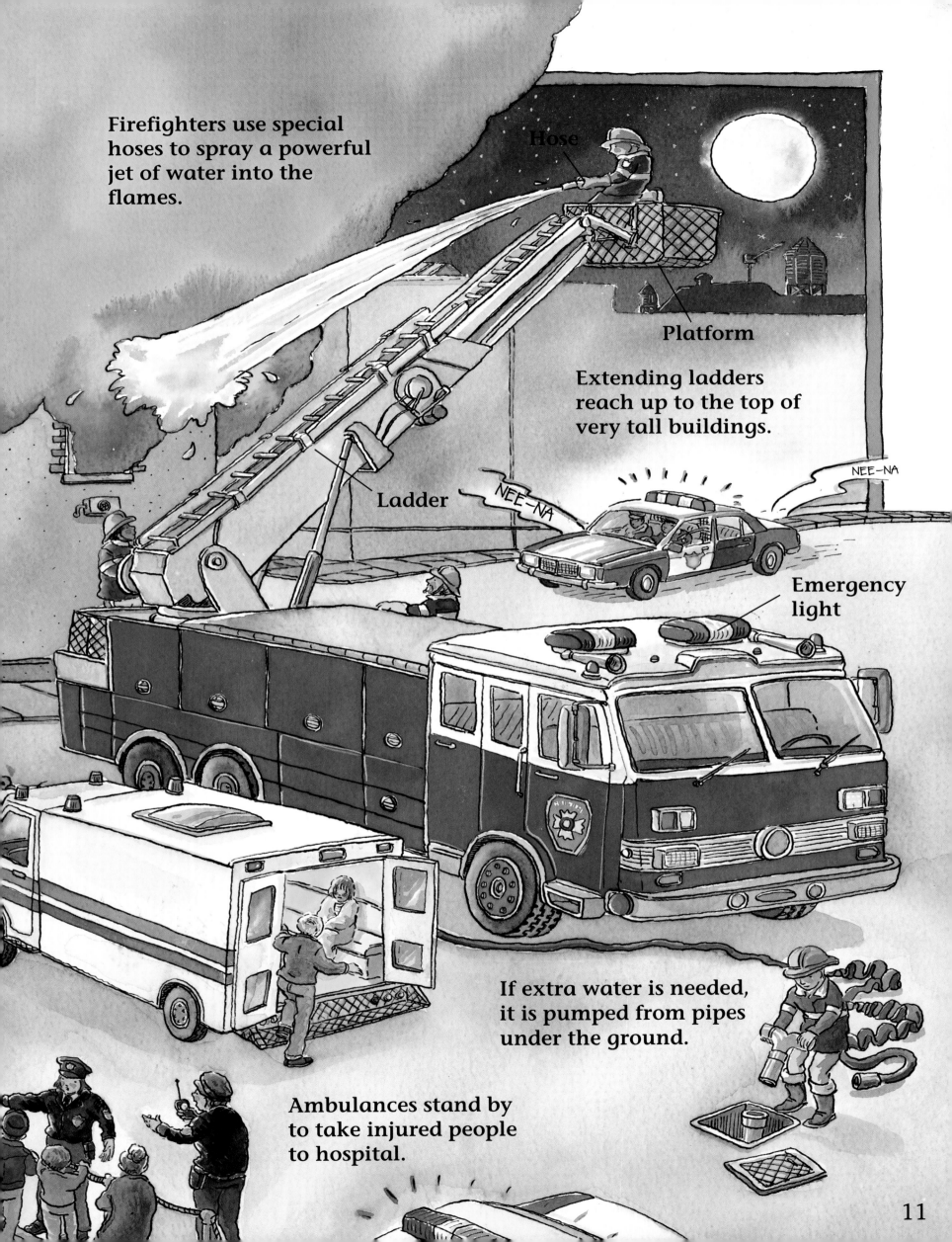

Firefighters use special hoses to spray a powerful jet of water into the flames.

Hose

Platform

Extending ladders reach up to the top of very tall buildings.

Ladder

NEE-NA

NEE-NA

Emergency light

If extra water is needed, it is pumped from pipes under the ground.

Ambulances stand by to take injured people to hospital.

Dumpers and diggers

Special machines are used to make roads and tunnels or build houses and bridges. These machines are very powerful. They help us to dig, lift, carry and pull.

Driver's cabin

A concrete mixer makes concrete by mixing cement, sand and gravel inside a big revolving drum.

Bulldozers have wide shovels to clear away soil and rock.

Bucket

Diggers have buckets with sharp metal teeth for gouging into hard earth.

Working machines

Street sweepers brush up dirt from our streets.

Dump trucks carry loads of rock or earth. Their thick tyres help them move easily over bumpy or muddy ground.

Tipping bucket

Wing mirror

Hydraulic arm

Driver's cabin

Safety mesh

Deep-tread tyres

Dustbin lorries collect rubbish from our homes.

Snow ploughs clear snow and scatter grit.

Tractors pull ploughs and trailers on farms.

Combine harvesters cut down crops such as wheat.

Crane trucks load and unload heavy goods.

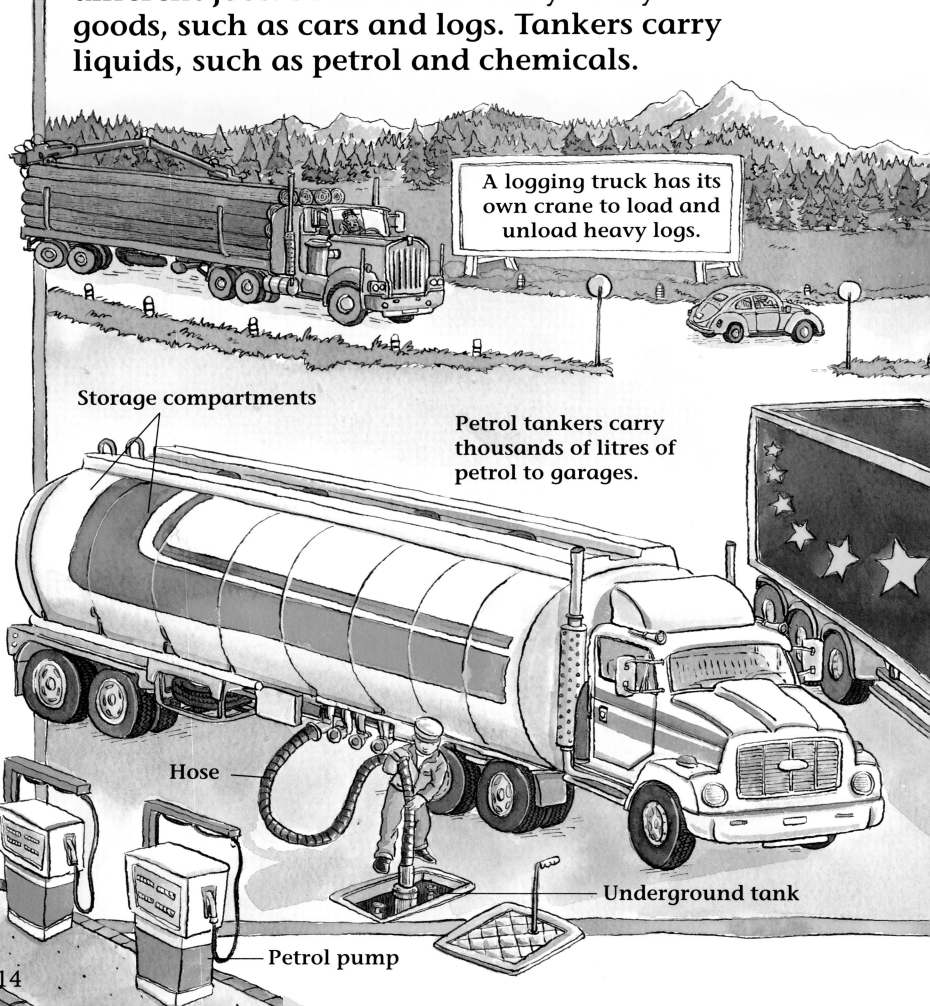

Road train

Trucks and tankers

Trucks and tankers come in all shapes and sizes. They are specially designed to do different jobs. Some trucks carry bulky goods, such as cars and logs. Tankers carry liquids, such as petrol and chemicals.

A logging truck has its own crane to load and unload heavy logs.

Storage compartments

Petrol tankers carry thousands of litres of petrol to garages.

Hose

Underground tank

Petrol pump

Life on the road

Truck drivers keep in touch using a radio-telephone.

On long trips, the driver sleeps in a bunk bed at the back of the cab.

The driver hands over delivery papers when the truck is unloaded.

Car transporters take new cars from a factory to a showroom.

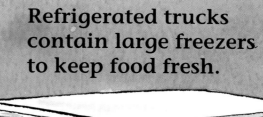

Refrigerated trucks contain large freezers to keep food fresh.

Trailer

Trailer hook

Fuel tank

Tractor unit

Mirror

An articulated truck has two parts – a tractor unit and a trailer. The trailer is a large container which carries the load. The tractor unit has a powerful engine to pull the trailer along.

Small boats

SPLISH, SPLASH, SPLOSH!

All kinds of boats travel on or through the water. Some have sails to catch the wind. Others have engines to give them speed.

Coastguards patrol coastal waters to make sure that people are safe.

A windsurfer moves the sail so that the wind hits it and pushes the board forward.

Speedboats can go so fast, their hulls lift out of the water.

A rowing boat is pulled through the water by oars.

Oar

Which boat?

A catamaran is a racing boat with two hulls.

Only one of these boats is powered by an engine. Do you know which one?

Yacht

Speedboat

Rowing boat

Canoe

Sail

Tiller

Stern

Bow

Hull

Most people learn to sail in small sailing boats called dinghys.

All sailing boats have triangular-shaped sails to catch the wind.

Sailing boats can sail in any direction, except straight into the wind.

A busy port

Large boats and ships sail into sheltered ports and harbours to load and unload their cargo and passengers. Such big ships need deep water to move in.

Dredgers scoop mud from the bottom of the port to keep the water deep.

Dredger

Tugboats guide ships into port.

Some ferries carry cars as well as passengers.

Fishing boat

High-speed ferries

There are different kinds of fast ferries.

A hydrofoil scoots across the water on giant skis.

A hovercraft floats just above the sea on a huge bag of air.

A jetfoil skims over the water on special underwater "wings".

Large gantry cranes load and unload the ship's cargo. Cargo usually travels in big steel containers.

Gantry crane

Driver's cabin

Container ship

Containers may be carrying cars, food or machines.

Container

Straddler carrier

Freight train

Straddler carriers pick up the containers and load them on to lorries and freight trains.

Lorry

An ocean liner

Ocean liners are like giant floating hotels. They cruise across the sea carrying thousands of holidaymakers and hundreds of crew. It is the crew's job to look after the holidaymakers and the ship.

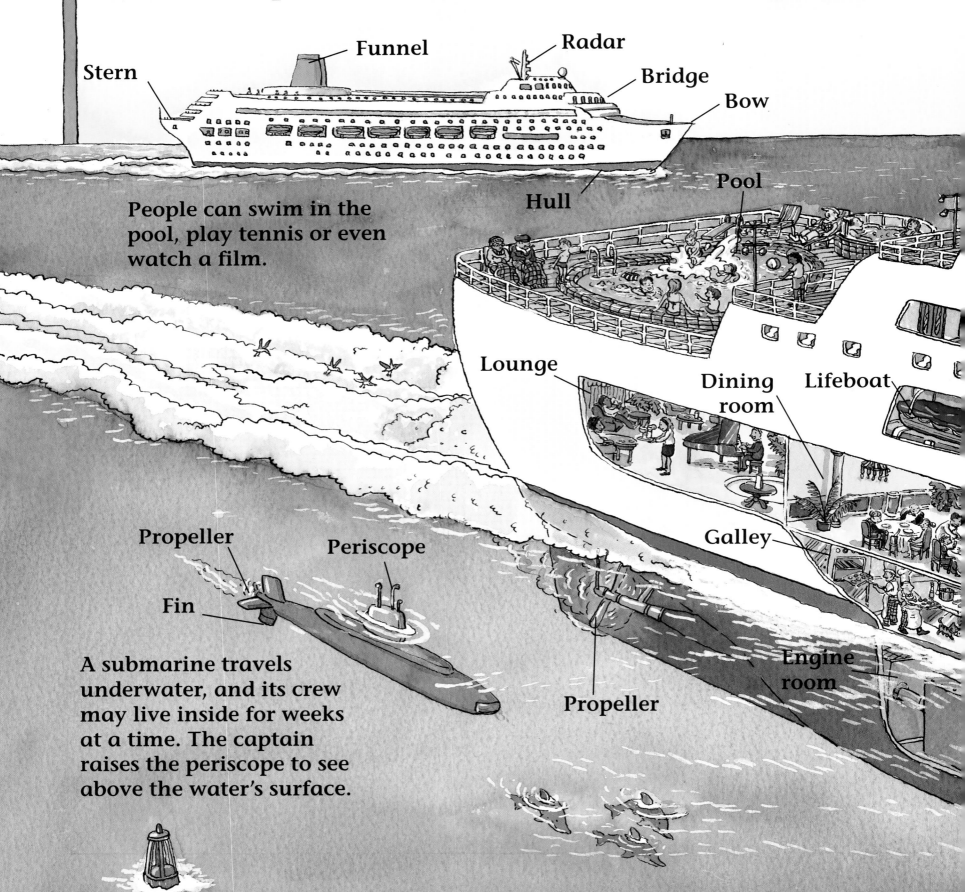

Funnel

Radar

Stern

Bridge

Bow

Hull

Pool

People can swim in the pool, play tennis or even watch a film.

Lounge

Dining room

Lifeboat

Propeller

Periscope

Fin

Galley

A submarine travels underwater, and its crew may live inside for weeks at a time. The captain raises the periscope to see above the water's surface.

Propeller

Engine room

Sailing a liner

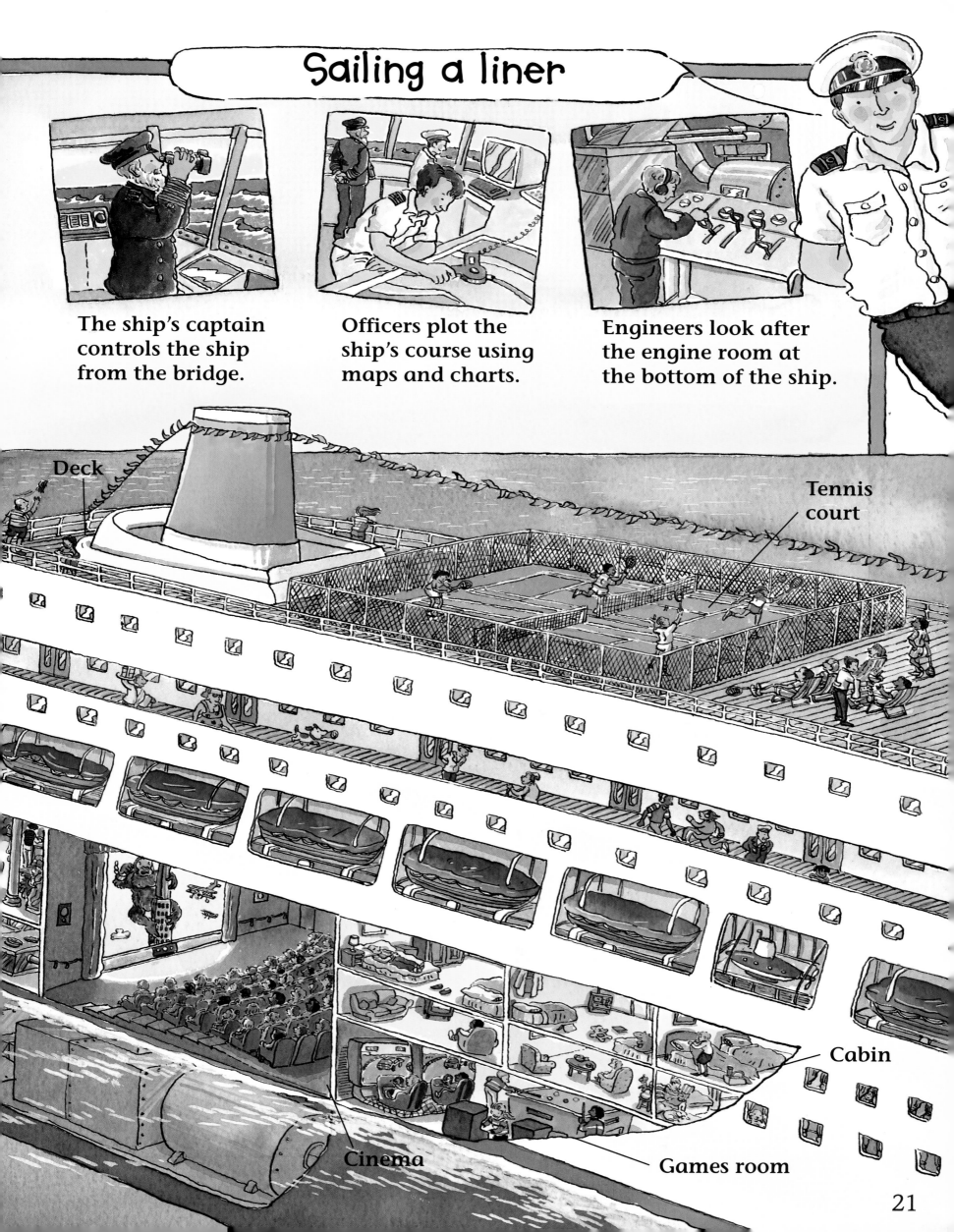

The ship's captain controls the ship from the bridge.

Officers plot the ship's course using maps and charts.

Engineers look after the engine room at the bottom of the ship.

Deck

Tennis court

Cabin

Cinema

Games room

All kinds of trains

CHOO! CHOO! CHOO!

Trains hurtle along on metal rails. Some carry goods, called freight, across whole countries. Others carry passengers, letters and parcels between towns and cities.

Cable cars hang from electric cables.

Car transporter

Coal wagon

Container wagon

Chemical wagon

Passenger carriage

Diesel train

Diesel trains burn oil to make electricity. Electricity powers the train.

Tram tracks

Trams are buses on rails. They carry people around busy towns.

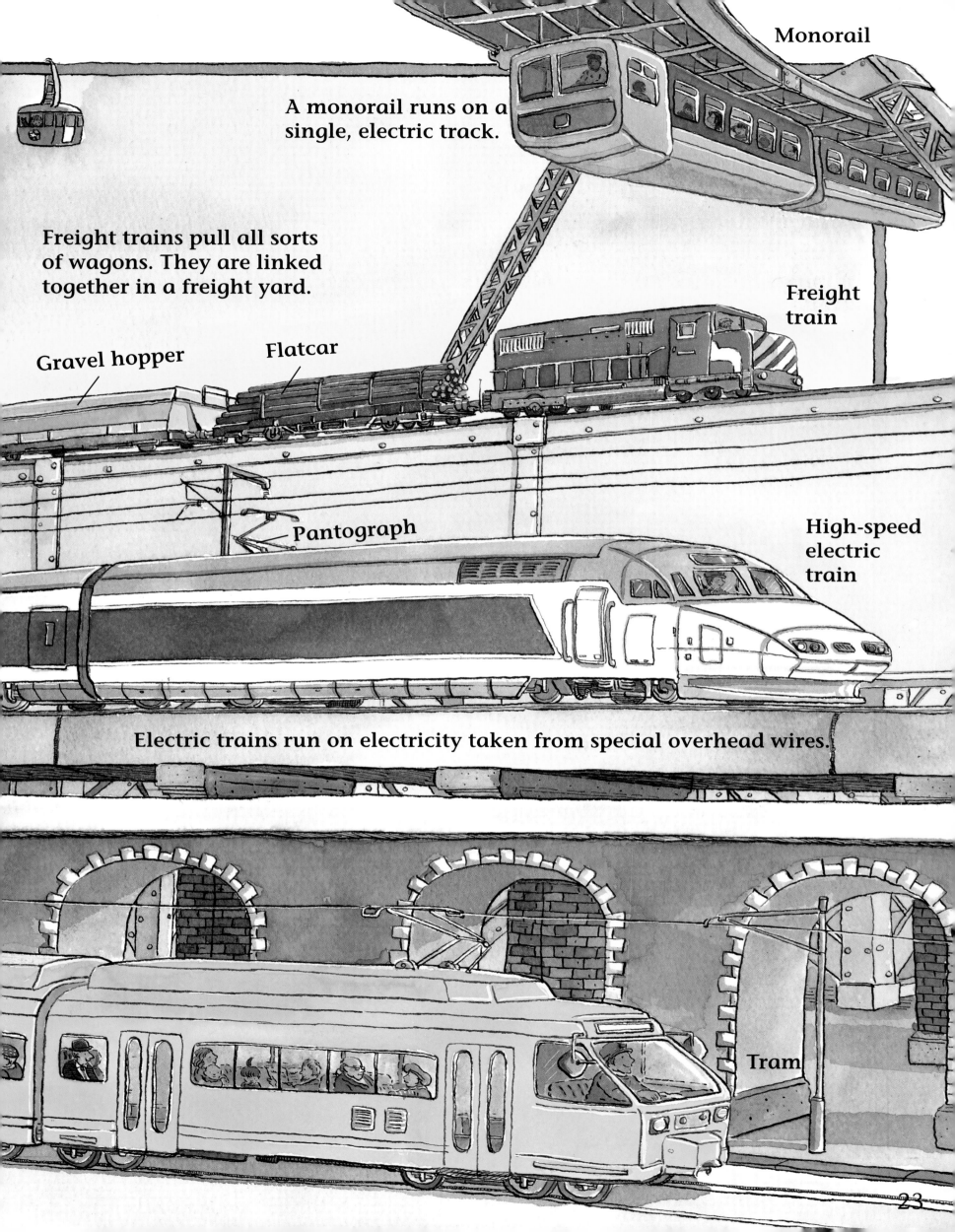

Monorail

A monorail runs on a single, electric track.

Freight trains pull all sorts of wagons. They are linked together in a freight yard.

Freight train

Gravel hopper

Flatcar

Pantograph

High-speed electric train

Electric trains run on electricity taken from special overhead wires.

Tram

23

Going underground

Underneath many large cities are hundreds of kilometres of railway tracks. Travelling below the busy, traffic-filled streets is often the fastest way to get about.

Lifts or moving stairs called escalators carry people down to the platform.

Emergency stairs

Escalator

There's a driver's cabin at each end of the train.

Platform

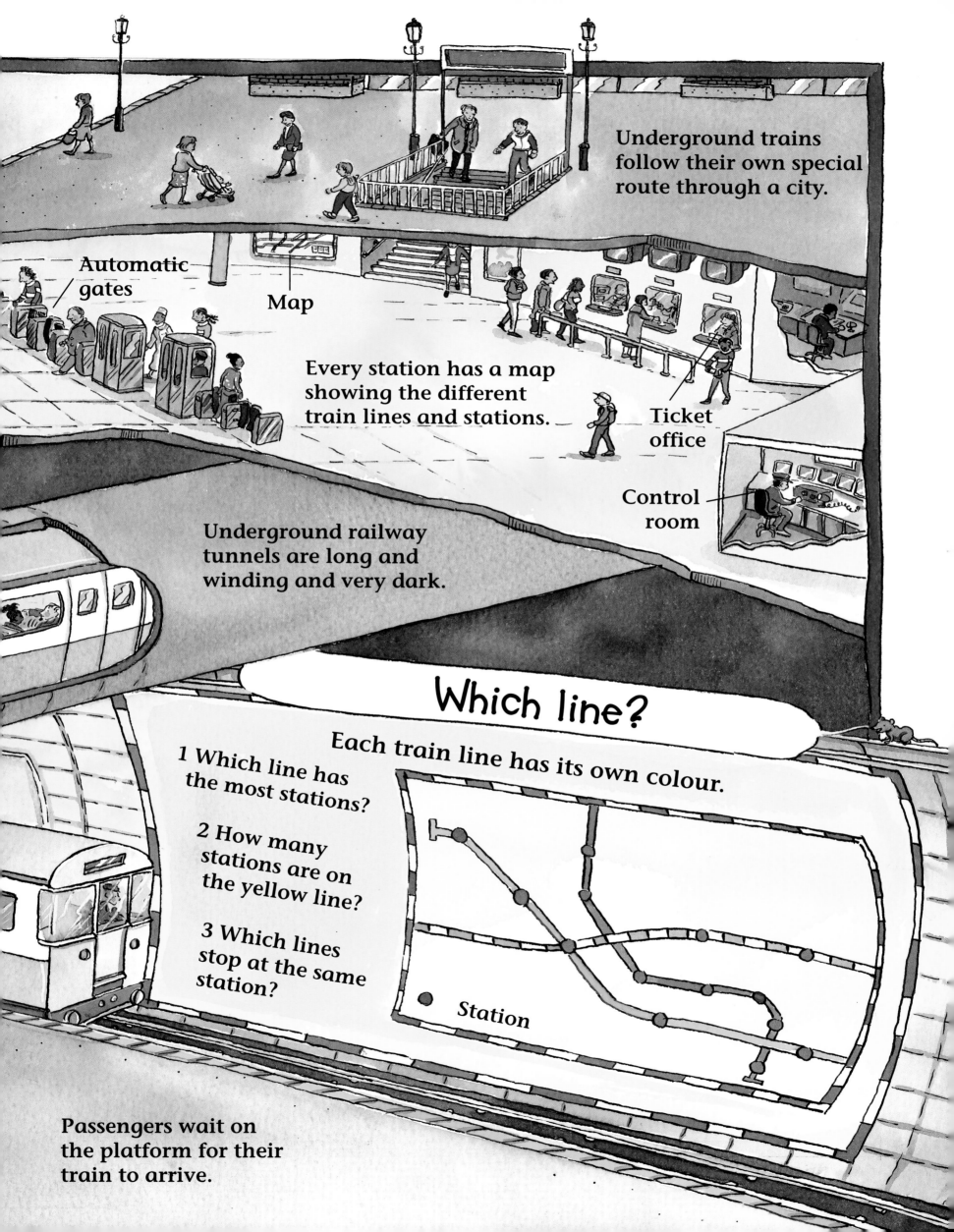

Underground trains follow their own special route through a city.

Automatic gates

Map

Every station has a map showing the different train lines and stations.

Ticket office

Control room

Underground railway tunnels are long and winding and very dark.

Which line?

Each train line has its own colour.

1 Which line has the most stations?

2 How many stations are on the yellow line?

3 Which lines stop at the same station?

Station

Passengers wait on the platform for their train to arrive.

Superplanes

Planes carry passengers and cargo high up into the clouds, above houses, towns and cities. They are the fastest way of travelling from one place to another.

Commuter jet

Passenger terminal

Control tower

The Super Guppy carries rockets and aircraft parts.

Passenger walkway

Hold

Before the passengers can board a plane, it must be cleaned and re-fuelled. Baggage is stored in the hold.

Planes wait until the controllers in the control tower say they can go. Then they zoom down the runway and take off.

Concorde is the world's fastest passenger plane.

Runway

Jumbo jet

GB814

The plane's engines drive the plane forward, and the air pushing under and around its wings helps to lift it into the sky.

All kinds of planes

Sea planes can take off and land on water.

The Harrier can take off straight into the air.

Light aircraft are used to spray crops.

Flying machines

Not everything that flies has an engine and wings. Balloons simply need hot air to help them travel across the sky. Gliders and hang-gliders soar on rising currents of warm air.

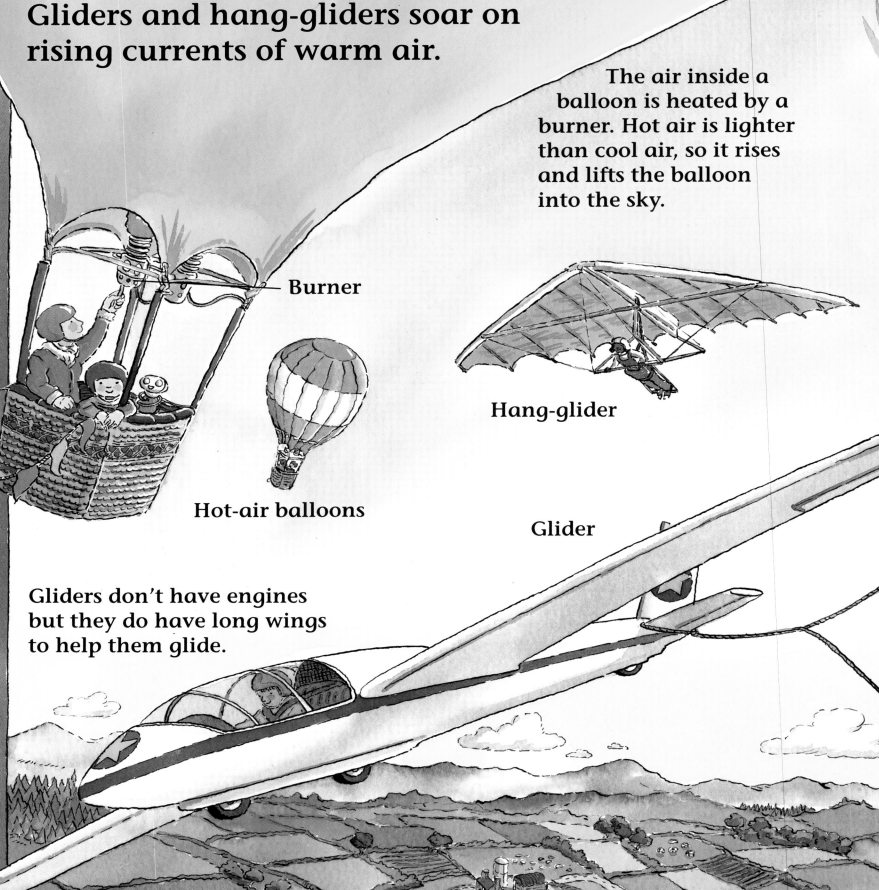

The air inside a balloon is heated by a burner. Hot air is lighter than cool air, so it rises and lifts the balloon into the sky.

Burner

Hang-glider

Hot-air balloons

Glider

Gliders don't have engines but they do have long wings to help them glide.

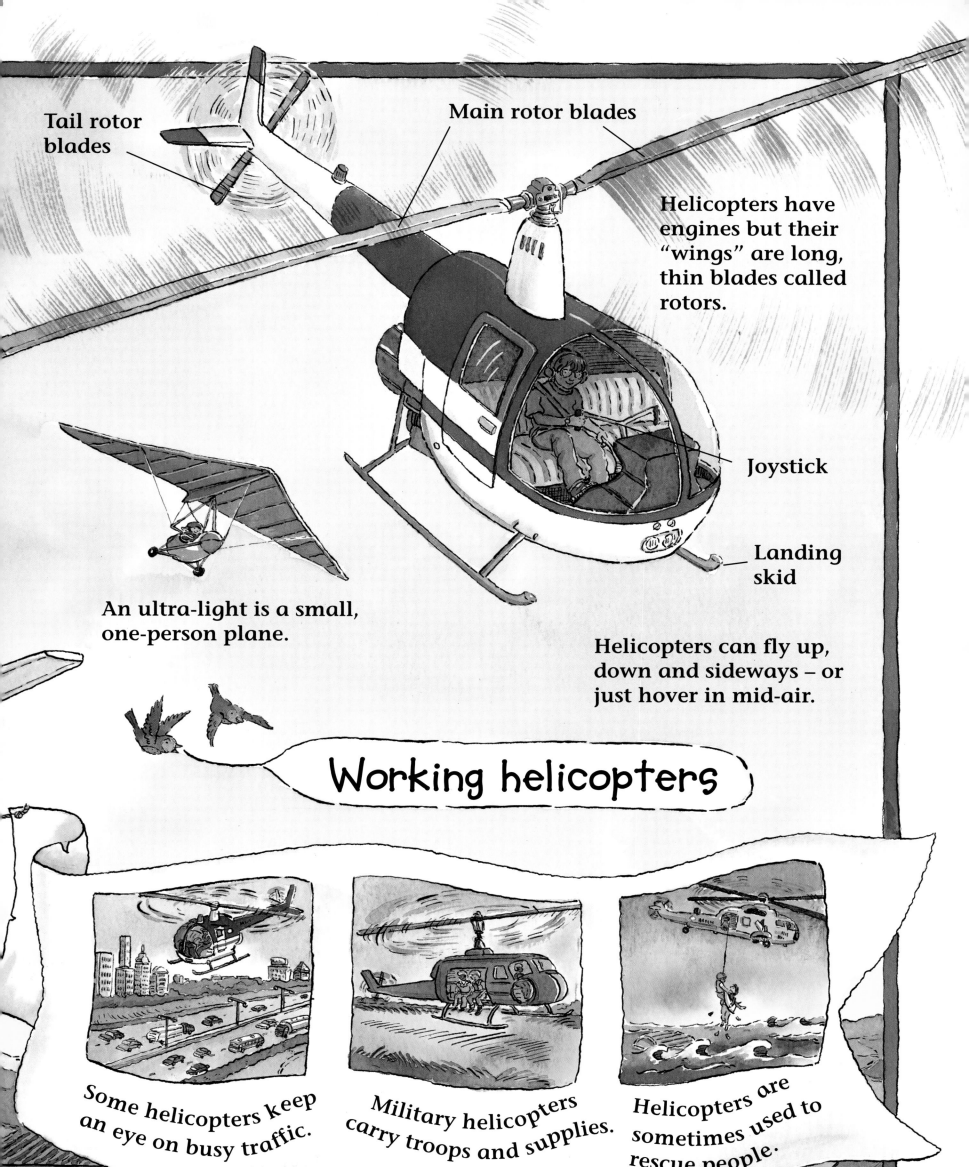

Tail rotor blades

Main rotor blades

Helicopters have engines but their "wings" are long, thin blades called rotors.

Joystick

An ultra-light is a small, one-person plane.

Landing skid

Helicopters can fly up, down and sideways – or just hover in mid-air.

Working helicopters

Some helicopters keep an eye on busy traffic.

Military helicopters carry troops and supplies.

Helicopters are sometimes used to rescue people.

Travelling in space

Astronauts travel into space, as far as the Moon and beyond, in special machines called spacecraft. Their job is to learn how to live and work in space. Perhaps someday soon, we'll all become space travellers.

Viking – landed on Mars.

Marina 10 – reached Venus and Mercury.

Tiny spacecraft called probes are sent into space to explore faraway planets. They don't carry any people.

Voyager – sent back pictures of the planets Uranus, Saturn, Jupiter and Neptune.

Lift off!

1 The space shuttle zooms into space.

2 The two booster rockets fall away.

3 The main fuel tank falls away when its fuel is used up.

4 The shuttle returns to Earth and lands like a plane.

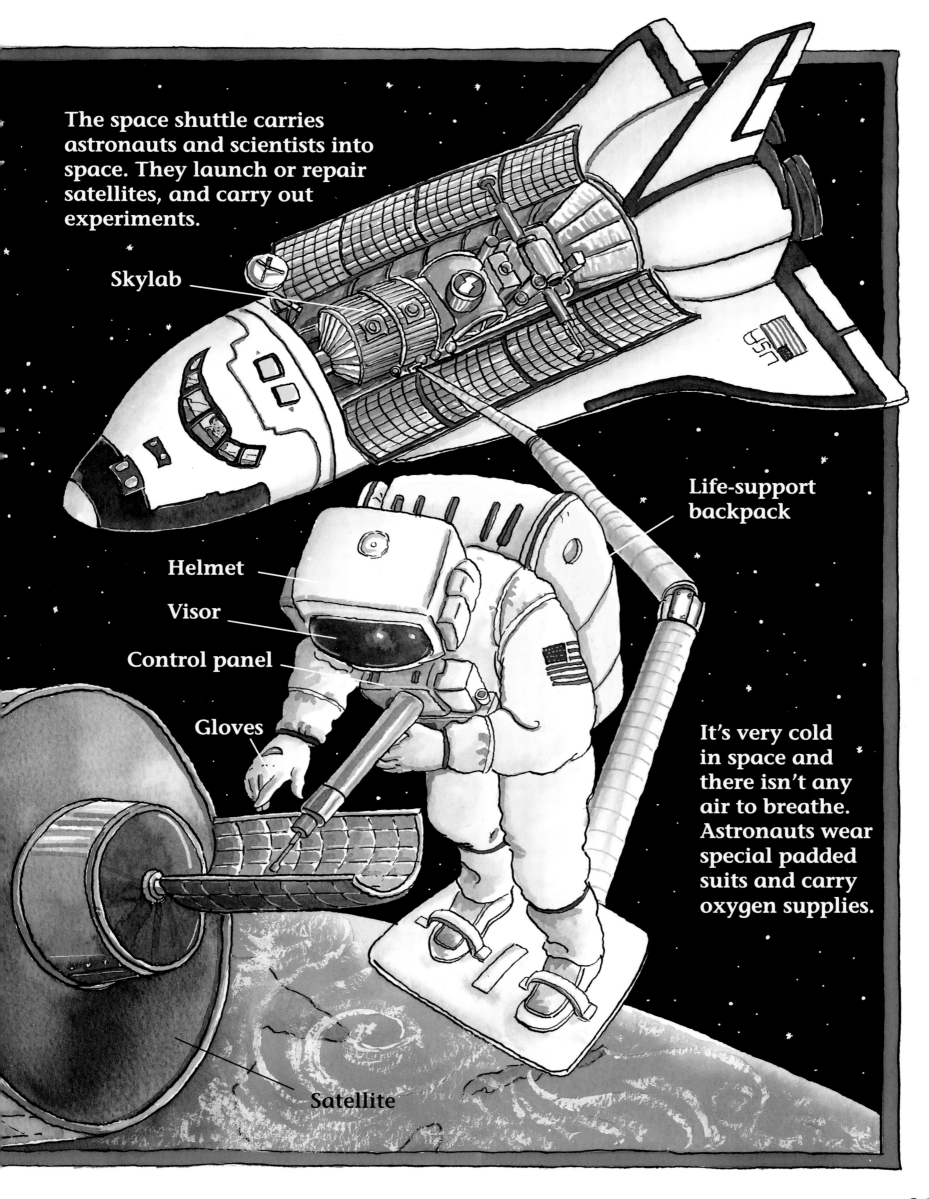

The space shuttle carries astronauts and scientists into space. They launch or repair satellites, and carry out experiments.

Skylab

Life-support backpack

Helmet

Visor

Control panel

Gloves

It's very cold in space and there isn't any air to breathe. Astronauts wear special padded suits and carry oxygen supplies.

Satellite

Index

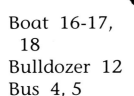

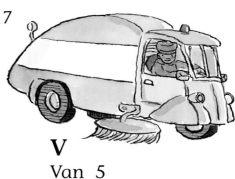